RESCUE DOGS and REAL ESTATE

Steve Schlueter

with

Tammi Juengst
and Shelly Shea

Contents

Steve Schlueter

Note from the Author

Rescue Dogs and Real Estate is a fictional story about Michael Barnes, a real estate agent whose life and business are out of control. He knows things need to change, but he doesn't quite know how to change them. Michael's story was inspired by my own experiences and the experiences of clients that I've coached through the years.

Back in 2008, I was asked to shadow superstar coach Tony DiCello during the tour for Gary Keller's book, *SHIFT*. When the subject of databases came up, DiCello asked the seven hundred members of the audience to stand up if they were contacting the people in their database thirty-three or more times per year, via email, personal contact, phone call, or direct mail. To our surprise, only around fifteen percent of the room stood up. He then asked them to remain standing if they had had at least four *actual conversations* per year with the people in their database. I was shocked to see how few people remained standing.

Tony and I conducted this informal polling with other audiences across the country. We learned that roughly three to five percent of agents actively engaged with their network, sphere of influence, and past clients. Most agents were operating in a manner that was more transaction-based and less relationship-based.

This realization led me to develop a system we call "DTD2," or "Doing the Database Two," to help sales professionals build relationship-based businesses. DTD2 is part of a larger system, called "Never Ending Referrals." I designed this system after spending more than 14,000 hours as a real estate coach, trainer, and multi-office brokerage operator and seeing what works for agents today. What we are noticing is an increasing demand for professionals who can build strong relationships, and these are the strategies and systems that can prepare agents for this rapidly changing landscape.

Thanks for reading,
Steve Schlueter

Chapter 1

The Exercise

It was Saturday, January 1, the first day of the new year. Michael Barnes sat at his desk, wearing his favorite gray sweats and warm sheepskin slippers. It was a cold, dreary morning with a chance of rain. He watched the marshmallows dissolve into froth on the surface of his hot chocolate. Glancing at his calendar, he realized he'd never been more relieved to turn the page. The past year had been tough, and he hoped that the new year would be the time of renewal and reinvention he so desperately needed.

Michael's business was struggling, and he was working hard to scratch out a meager living. He tried to pinpoint where things had gone wrong. He certainly had his share of obstacles to overcome through the years.

Michael thought about the day, back in middle school, when his dad sat him and his younger brother down at the kitchen table and told them that their mom had pancreatic cancer. She was gone within three months, and their family was shattered. Their father fell into a depression, leaving Michael and his younger brother largely unsupervised.

The lack of structure at home meant no one was checking up on Michael's grades in school, and he was perfectly happy being a "C" student if it meant he could focus on the things he enjoyed.

In high school, Michael found a way to avoid the academic grind by enrolling in the automotive vocational program. Michael was enamored with the classic cars he saw in hot rod magazines and hoped to turn his hobby into a career. He worked a couple of jobs and managed to save up enough money to buy his first car, a '69 Chevelle. She was a bit of a beater, but he dreamed about one day restoring her to her former muscle-car glory.

Nearly a decade later, twenty-eight-year-old Michael was working as an auto mechanic, spending twelve-hour days in a sweltering repair shop. The job was dirty and demanding, just like his boss, Gus. This angry and impatient man made Michael's life miserable. Michael was desperate to escape. One Sunday afternoon, he was looking at job postings in the newspaper when he noticed an ad for real estate sales. The ad read, "Be your own boss." Those words were all he needed to read. He immediately called and registered for the next "Careers and Coffee" open house.

Up until that point, Michael's only experience with real estate was he and his brother inheriting a piece of land from a relative. The boys had quickly sold the property, leaving each of them with a $40,000 windfall, which gave him the seed money he needed to *do something different*. After the "Careers and Coffee" session, Michael decided to give his old job and Gus the boot and *be his own boss*.

Michael could hardly believe that seven years had passed since his days in the shop. His first year in real estate was a struggle, but in the fourth quarter of that year, he attended a conference where he learned about expired listings. He learned the scripts, dialogues, and tactics that would launch his success. In his second full year in real estate, Michael did 42 transactions, and 32 of those were expired listings. He had truly found himself *in the zone*, a place that worked for him, and he was excited about real estate being his new career.

But now sitting at his desk, a new year upon him—what would be his eighth year in the business—he suddenly felt like it had all slipped away from him. Just three years earlier, expired listings were abundant, but the market had shifted in recent years, and he now found himself in a full-blown seller's market. The supply of homes for sale was at an all-time low, and buyers were scooping up the available inventory at record speed.

Back in the good old days, Michael's focus had been on obtaining seller listings. When expired listings became scarce, he became desperate and resorted to buying leads from the big Internet portals. Michael realized that he was paying a heavy price for those leads, both financially and in the amount of time and energy required to convert them. Real estate was just not fun anymore. He missed the feeling he used to get from walking in the door of an expired listing and then walking out with the listing agreement. Overnight it had turned into hard, frustrating work.

As Michael sipped his hot cocoa, he resolved to make it a better year. Two weeks earlier, Michael had heard a podcast by one of his favorite authors. The title, "New Year, New You," had caught his attention, and he hung on every word. The host recommended listeners do an exercise, one based on a personal development ritual he had been doing for two decades. With nothing to lose, Michael decided to take on the challenge. The exercise required that he set aside New Year's Day as a day of uninterrupted reflection.

Michael pulled out both his old school Day-Timer and his electronic calendar. He was instructed to go through each day of the previous year and make notes about what each day offered in the way of lessons and experiences. If his year had been a football game, what would be on the highlight reel? What about the blooper reel? With whom should he spend more time? Whom should he avoid? What valuable lessons did he take away? Most importantly, what would he do differently in the upcoming year?

As Michael reviewed his calendar, he was disappointed by how few appointments he'd had. He thought he had adjusted to the market, but the numbers didn't lie. These adjustments didn't translate into new business, or at least, not enough of it. There had to be a better way to make a living. Should he venture down a new career path? Michael didn't feel as though he had many options. Where does a guy without a college degree find a good job, anyway?

Michael forced himself back into the exercise. The deeper he went, the more he realized that his life and business were out of control. He worked his way through the days, weeks, and months, but stopped suddenly when he came to August 27th. He sat quietly for a moment, then reached for a tissue as tears rolled down his face.

The 27th was Tonya's birthday, and she had looked forward to spending the day with him. She had hoped that he had a special celebration planned for her. After two years together, she even fantasized that he might propose.

Tonya was part of a tight-knit family that was full of hugs and family rituals. She was one of six kids, a group of siblings who spent a lot of time together, even as adults. Unlike Michael, Tonya had excelled in school. She was a physical therapist with her own private practice. Her patients adored her because she poured her heart into helping them heal. Tonya was a big personality in a small package and had a million-dollar smile that lit up a room.

In the days and weeks leading up to Tonya's birthday, Michael was busy chasing deals and not paying attention to his personal life. On the day of her birthday, Tonya was waiting at home alone. It was after nine when Michael finally called. Even then, he didn't remember that it was her birthday.

That was the last straw for Tonya. She saw too many things in Michael that were out of alignment with her values. She believed that family and relationships should come first. Michael was a workaholic who was unwilling to treat her like a priority. Tonya decided to move in a new direction, one that did not include Michael.

Steve Schlueter

Chapter 2

Sophie

Michael pulled himself together and went back to his calendar, starting on August 28th, the day after Tonya's birthday. After about an hour, he came to an entry that put a smile on his face. It was October 28th, just two months after his breakup with Tonya. He recalled that day so clearly. He was home alone, listening to the radio, and feeling lonely. He was starving for companionship but just wasn't ready to start dating again. The last thing he wanted to do was fail in another relationship. He knew he had to work on himself first.

Michael heard a public service announcement for the local no-kill shelter. They were having a big adoption drive that weekend. Michael decided to visit the shelter, just to have a look.

Growing up, Michael had begged his mom for a dog. After she passed away, his dad could barely care for himself and his sons, much less a pet. "Adult" Michael always knew that one day he would have the dog he had wanted since he was a kid.

Sunday, October 29th was a clear and crisp autumn day, perfect for a visit to the animal shelter. As he drove, Michael wondered what kind of dog he would want *if* he were to get one. He wasn't sure but decided he would just *know* when he saw the *right one*. As Michael walked from kennel to kennel, he noticed some dogs would rush toward him with their tails wagging, while others were too timid to approach the fence. Michael decided he wanted a dog with a big personality and a playful spirit, sort of a dog-version of Tonya.

Just when he was about to give up, he spotted a small, thin dog with dirty fur looking over at him. She was black with tan markings on her face, chest, and tail. She immediately engaged with him, practically begging for his attention. She put her paws up on the gate, and her tail was wagging at ninety miles an hour. She began licking his fingers as he reached out to pet her. He felt an immediate connection to her, so he asked the attendant if he could take her to the "off-leash" area.

As soon as they entered the fence, he set her free. She ran around the yard as though she knew she was auditioning for the part of his playful, spirited companion. She circled the large, grassy yard until she wore herself out, coming to rest at Michael's feet. Her spirit and unbridled joy lifted Michael from the sadness that had dominated the past two months of his life.

Michael learned about his dog's history as he completed the various adoption forms, with the volunteer explaining that the dog had recently finished weaning five puppies. This explained why she was underweight. Her puppies had all been adopted. Michael wished that he could've seen the puppies but was relieved that he wasn't tempted into adopting the entire litter. The shelter had acquired this mama dog from a kill shelter while she was still pregnant. She was moved to the no-kill shelter just in the nick of time, as she and her unborn puppies were in the next group of animals scheduled to be euthanized. Michael had never thought much about the number of animals that were euthanized daily in every city.

Michael and his new companion headed home with a starter kit that included a leash, collar, and a small bag of food. The shelter also gave Michael an information packet with care tips and coupons, along with her vet records. The car ride home gave this sweet momma dog a chance to nap peacefully on the passenger seat after an exciting day.

Michael looked over his calendar entries for the days immediately following the adoption. He had spent some time looking at pictures online, trying to figure out her breed. He decided she was a Miniature Manchester Terrier mix. She had the looks and all the personality traits of a terrier, loving to see squirrels and small chipmunks when out for her walk, and making a distinct prey sound any time she saw small rodents.

He decided to rename his new fur baby. The shelter had named her "Honey," but he thought that was odd since her fur was mostly black.

He noticed how she loved to sit on the back of the sofa, like a cat. From her perch, she could enjoy the view through the window and survey what was going on around the room. When he told a friend about how his beautiful new dog found her *spot* on top of the sofa, all of a sudden it hit him... sofa, *sofa*...Sophie! Which is how Sophie got her name.

Michael finished up his year in review and felt like there had been more lowlights than highlights over the past year. Yet, as he saw Sophie sleeping at his feet, he realized how grateful he was to have his new companion. He recognized that he hadn't been the greatest doggy dad and resolved to be a more responsible pet owner. He went online and scheduled an appointment for a checkup that was three weeks overdue. Then he gave her a warm bath, something that probably should have been done a week earlier. Once the care duties were done, he decided they both needed a change of scenery.

He looked down at Sophie and promised to take her to the dog park the following day.

Chapter 3

Hardberger Park

The next morning, Michael woke up with a renewed spirit and improved energy. He resolved to focus on what he could control and give up worrying about the things that were outside of his control. He had promised Sophie that he would take her to the dog park, but the forecast was for the dreary and drizzly weather to continue for the next few days. Michael decided to stay in, build a fire, and watch some football. He also spent some time working with Sophie.

It took little effort to coax Sophie to sit and speak on command. *The power of dog treats is incredible!* he thought.

They managed to take a walk during a break in the weather. She loved to run and practically dragged him down the street. She was walking him! She pulled so hard that the collar tightened against her throat and made her cough. Michael decided to make a trip to the pet store to find her a harness before she hurt herself.

Thursday morning brought much better weather, so Michael and Sophie finally got their chance to try out the dog park. After wrapping up a few work tasks and picking up around the house, Michael loaded Sophie into his Tahoe and headed out. He was eager to let Sophie run off-leash and to watch her interact with some new dog friends.

As Michael fired up his seven-year-old Chevy Tahoe, he was distracted by the glow of the tire pressure warning light. The message center on the dash reminded him that an oil change was also overdue. He stared at his odometer, which read 132,311 miles and thought, *This thing is on its last leg.*

He managed to keep his Tahoe clean for chauffeuring buyers around, but it wasn't as well taken care of as it should have been. He dreamt about replacing his old, tired SUV with the new Cadillac Escalade he'd been eyeing. He resigned himself to the fact that a new vehicle was simply not in the budget at the time. He was going to have to keep the Tahoe plugging along for at least another year.

He stopped at the tire shop for service, only to learn that the tread depth was below safe operating limits. The attendant showed him the treadwear chart and advised him to replace two tires immediately. It was an unexpected, frustrating expense.

As he waited for the crew to replace the tires, Michael said to himself, *Dude, you've got to get it together! Too many things are being neglected.*

He pledged to maintain the tires' air pressure so they would wear evenly, and to get them rotated routinely. The tire shop offered him a package where he could pay a flat fee and have the rotation performed whenever needed. Even Michael could stick to that simple plan.

With their tire shop troubles behind them, Michael and Sophie finally made it to the pet superstore. Sophie trotted up and down the aisles alongside Michael, taking in all the smells. Michael surveyed the giant warehouse, amazed at the selection and variety of pet supplies. There was something for every kind of pet imaginable.

What exactly does one do with a pet scorpion? Michael wondered as he passed the arachnid section.

After looking at the various harnesses, Michael chose a bright pink harness that fit Sophie's spirited personality to a tee. He also got a long, retractable leash that would allow her some freedom, yet lock her down when he needed to keep her safe by his side. The forecast called for cold weather in the weeks ahead, giving Michael the perfect excuse to buy her a cute dog sweater.

As Michael and Sophie pulled up to Hardberger Park, it seemed like everyone in town must have had the same idea. After several days of wintry weather, people were eager to get out with their pets. After Michael finally found a parking spot, they walked down the trail to the off-leash area. He realized that there were two fenced areas: one for large dogs and another for small dogs. Michael, after seeing two Great Danes and a German Shepherd roughhousing, felt grateful for the small dog section. He imagined that his little Sophie would be scared to death if she were forced to play with the big dogs.

They passed through the gate into the play yard, and Michael unhooked Sophie's leash. She was ecstatic! She ran in circles, dug in the leaves, and engaged some of the other dogs in a game of chase. Sophie loved the freedom of the off-leash area. Obedience? She checked that at the gate! She didn't come when called. She didn't sit, she didn't listen. She was just having the time of her life in her own little doggie world.

Michael settled in on a bench and tried to adopt Sophie's carefree attitude. As he watched her play, his mind drifted back to business. He was excited about the new listing he'd gotten but didn't feel like he had a grand plan for the year. He just couldn't see how it was all going to work out. He'd had to scratch out a living the year before, and worried that the coming year would be more of the same.

He thought, *Maybe I just have to keep buying leads until the market shifts back toward my strengths.*

The clank of the entry gate disrupted Michael's thoughts. He looked up and saw a familiar face. It was Mandi Miller, an agent that he'd met back in September. Michael had sold one of her listings, and he remembered how cool and confident she had seemed throughout their transaction. He was impressed with how she handled her business, and how her assistant made everything run so smoothly. It was, without question, the most seamless transaction he'd had in the last several years. She had been the consummate professional.

Mandi immediately recognized Michael. She flashed him a smile as she stopped at the fountain to give her little Shih Tzu a drink. Michael walked toward her to say hello, and Mandi introduced him to her dog, Gizmo. Gizmo was quick to respond to Mandi's commands and seemed like a well-behaved dog. As Gizmo ran off to play with the other dogs, Michael invited Mandi to sit with him on the bench to chat.

After a few minutes, Mandi asked, "How's business going for you?"

Michael spared the details, but said, "Well, you know, things could be better. The market's been a little crazy. Every seller is getting multiple offers, making things tough on buyers. I need more listings."

He then asked Mandi about her business.

She replied, "Well, I feel fortunate. Listings have been fairly abundant. In fact, I've already identified more than 30 clients that are likely to list with me this year. I'm looking forward to the year ahead because it is going to be my best year ever."

"Wow," he said. "You must be a lead generation machine. I used to get lots of expired listings, but those have pretty much dried up now that the market is so strong."

Mandi agreed, "I get it. It's a tight market right now. I used to get a lot of expired listings, too. I had gotten sucked into cold prospecting early in my career. Mostly out of necessity, especially with 'For Sale by Owners.' I still work a few of those, if they're in or around the area that I've been geo-farming. The fact is that a majority of my listings and sales these days come from repeat and referral business from my database."

Michael asked, "How do you manage your database? That sounds like a lot to keep up with."

"I couldn't do what I do without my transaction coordinator and my assistant," Mandi confessed. I give them 100% of the credit for keeping the systems consistent so that I'm able to reap the rewards. They free up my time and energy. My quality of life has drastically improved since I brought them into my business. They're like family to me. I'm so grateful for them."

Mandi was living the life that Michael aspired to live.

He turned to her and said, "Thank you for sharing your story. It's encouraging to hear that you've been successful despite the changes in the market. Last year was challenging for me. My old strategies aren't in alignment with the market. But this is the year I figure things out, even if I don't know where to start."

Michael's words resonated with Mandi. She knew exactly how he was feeling. Just four years earlier, her business was inconsistent and unpredictable. She struggled with her database. She had been prospecting cold leads, yet lacked a long-term approach to her business that was sustainable and repeatable. Hearing Michael talk, she realized she had been exactly where Michael was at this moment.

She felt grateful for the transformation she had undergone, and for the mentor who'd helped her find her way. She remembered her coach teaching her the importance of passing along what she had learned. He had encouraged her to be the light for someone else when the opportunity presented itself. Mandi realized that here was the opportunity.

She said to Michael, "I usually finish up my database calls around 1:30 or 2:00 on Thursdays, and then Gizmo and I come here to the dog park. Why don't you join us? We can talk about some of the things that we're doing in my office. Maybe it could help you have the kind of year that you're hoping to have. What do you say?"

Michael struggled with how to respond to Mandi's invitation. His limiting beliefs paralyzed him. Whatever Mandi was doing wouldn't work for him, he thought. He'd been out of touch with his database for too long. It was just another area of his life that he'd neglected. Now and then, he would send out a newsletter, but he knew that wasn't enough to stay connected with his database. Not like Mandi was. After all, he didn't have thirty listings lined up.

Michael stumbled on his words, "Thanks...I don't know if I can fit that in. But...thank you."

Mandi replied, "Well, I'll be here, weather permitting. If you change your mind, come join me. You do still have my cell number. Right?"

"Yeah."

"If I can ever help you, let me know", she said, as Sophie ran up for a drink of water.

Michael was uncomfortable. He felt like Mandi could somehow see his shortcomings. Michael remarked that it was getting late, snapped on Sophie's leash, and led her toward the exit.

He glanced over his shoulder and called out to Mandi with a polite, "Take care."

Chapter 4

The Beast

It was Thursday morning, and a week had passed since Michael bumped into Mandi and Gizmo at the dog park. It had been a great week for Michael and Sophie. Michael had spent time each day taking Sophie for walks and teaching her new commands. She would sit when prompted by Michael, especially if he had those tasty training treats in his pocket.

Her newest trick was sort of a ballerina twirl. It started when he held a treat about waist high, forcing her to stand on her back legs to reach it. She then spun around in a circle, following the pattern he made with his hand. It was the cutest pirouette he had ever seen. At times like these, he marveled at her intelligence and obedience. It was a different story, of course, when they were out for a walk and she spotted a squirrel or deer. That's when her inner terrier came out, and she set off on a prey-fueled sprint. He resolved to work with her on staying calm and coming when called.

Two o'clock came around, and Michael had to decide whether or not he and Sophie were going to meet Mandi and Gizmo at the dog park. He had enjoyed their last visit, but he felt a little intimidated by Mandi's success.

Fear got the best of him, and he decided he was *too busy* to meet Mandi. He opted instead to pursue the new Internet leads that came in from the portal. He told himself that his database was too far gone to benefit from Mandi's system.

Michael had developed many limiting beliefs around his database during his first year in real estate. At that time, his cubicle was located right next to the office's top agent, Gerri. People remembered Gerri for her big hair, big personality, and big smile. She was selling two or three homes a week, almost every week.

Gerri told Michael her secret to success. "Michael," she began, "if you want to have a career that lasts a lifetime, you need to be friends with your clients. You can start by sending them birthday cards or hosting a family-friendly event. Most importantly, enter them into your database and keep in touch with them. That will get you lots of referrals and repeat business."

All Michael could think at the time was, "I already have four friends! I don't need more friends. What I need are more buyers and sellers."

Gerri thought of Michael like a son and was always looking out for him. It was Gerri who had encouraged Michael to attend the regional convention, where he learned the things that would help him transform his struggling business.

At the time, residential real estate was in the throes of an extreme buyers' market. On the very first day of the conference, Michael realized there was an opportunity to be had in the pool of expired listings. On day two, in a breakout session, he learned about using scripts for connecting with clients. The speaker presented a few simple, yet effective, dialogues that Michael memorized and would put to use. Michael used the scripts to set listing appointments, overcome objections, and grow his business.

Michael's success with expired listings continued for just over four years. During that time, he bought himself a house and hired an assistant. Then came the inevitable market shift, when everything changed. Michael had bills to pay, so he was desperate to find new scripts and new tactics to keep the money coming in.

One day, Michael overheard his office mate, Chris, bragging about all the leads he was getting using the Internet. Michael envied Chris's apparent success, but he didn't like being around the man. Michael thought of Chris as arrogant and rude. In fact, Michael's secret nickname for him was "The Beast."

At 6'7", Chris O'Brien was an imposing man whose muscular arms were sprinkled with tattoos. He loved to brag about his athletic prowess, boring everyone with stories about his high school and college wrestling careers. He drove a big Audi A8, which he parked across two spots. He would disruptively burst into the office each morning to start working the phones. He even hired a couple of people, instructing them to "smile and dial" all day long. He had everyone convinced that converting Internet leads into sales is what funded his extravagant lifestyle.

Michael tried using paid leads to revive his business. He soon realized that the follow-up and long-term nurturing it took to convert those leads into sales was draining him. He told himself that the market would certainly shift again, and he'd go back to working expired listings. In the meantime, he just had to keep trying to make this work. He picked up the phone and started calling. He connected with a prospect that was tired of renting and starting to think about buying a home. He was proud of himself for being proactive but realized he was not quite performing like The Beast.

He checked his emails one last time and saw an invoice from one of the online portals. He studied it and was shocked by how much money he had been spending buying leads. The portal was also changing the rules by announcing that they were getting into brokerage, effectively becoming his competition. He could no longer justify spending his hard-earned money on unqualified leads. He felt defeated.

Michael reached up to his bookshelf and pulled down a manual from a class he had attended three years earlier. He attached sticky notes to the sections on "For Sale By Owners" (FSBOs) and "Geographic Farming." He headed home to spend some time with Sophie, taking the workbook with him. He decided that, over the weekend, he was going to build a system to convert listings from FSBOs as well as a plan for launching a geographic farm. Once again, Michael headed down a new path.

Chapter 5

The Call

It was mid-April. Wildflowers had started to pop up along the highways, and the trees were in full bloom. Michael had been spending more quality time with Sophie, including taking her to obedience training. He hadn't been able to train her to come when he called, and he worried that she might take off after a squirrel and get lost or run over by a car. Michael was proud of the progress she had made in the last two weeks. He was also proud of himself for stepping up and being a better *dog dad*. They had even been taking regular trips to the dog park...but not on Thursday afternoons. He didn't want to risk bumping into Mandi and Gizmo. As much as he wished he could have a successful business like Mandi's, he worried that she would tell him to "just be friends with his clients," the same advice Gerri had given him. It seemed easier to avoid Mandi than to face his fears.

Michael had been working hard on his for sale by owner (FSBO) project. In three months, he'd taken three listings and had a fourth one lined up for the following Thursday. The geographic farming, however, had been a much slower process. He had put together a couple of mail campaigns, bought some social media ads, and started a door-knocking schedule. He had gone to two appointments and hoped he could convert them into listings within sixty days. Michael wished things were moving more quickly, but at least he was working with sellers instead of chasing Internet leads like The Beast.

Michael's Thursday afternoon FSBO appointment went flawlessly. He skillfully handled every objection the client posed. He was so proud! The sellers were confident Michael was the professional they needed to sell their home quickly and for the most money possible. Michael felt energized as he headed back to the office to prepare the listing for entry into the MLS.

A call came in as Michael was driving, and he glanced at the dashboard display. "Maybe Jim Evans" it read. Michael took the call, even though he didn't remember anyone named Jim Evans. Jim reminded Michael that they had met about three years earlier at a sales seminar. They had sat together at lunch and chatted about the Chevelle that Michael was restoring. Jim mentioned to Michael that his mortgage company was sponsoring a charity car show and asked if Michael would like to be an exhibitor.

"A charity car show sounds great," Michael said. "But my Chevelle isn't exactly show-worthy. It's actually in storage right now. The transmission needs to be overhauled, and I just never got around to working on it."

Michael didn't tell Jim the whole story. He left out the part about being too busy chasing leads to spend time on his hobby. He also skipped the part about not having the extra money to fix up the Chevelle.

Jim encouraged Michael to come to the car show, even if he couldn't bring the Chevelle. The men chatted about business and hobbies for the next few minutes. The call ended as Michael arrived at his office. He paused to reflect on the conversation before getting out of the truck.

Interesting phone call, he thought. *Jim seems like a nice guy. He remembered so much about me, but I don't even remember meeting him.*

Michael hurried to get his listing entered so that he could get home and take a walk with Sophie.

As they meandered through the neighborhood, he thought more about the conversation with Jim. He reckoned he and Jim must have met at the seminar on FSBOs and Geo-Farming, but he still couldn't remember him. He certainly couldn't have picked him out of a police lineup. If he had run into him at the grocery store, he'd be just another stranger.

Michael wondered how it had happened that after a six-minute conversation he could feel such a connection with someone he didn't really know and hadn't spoken with in over three years. What had Jim said that put Michael at ease?

He had asked him where he was from, and how he came to live here. He asked him about his business and how he was adjusting to the current market. He also asked about his plans for the rest of the year and got him thinking about dusting off the old Chevelle and getting it fixed up.

Jim had listened to Michael as he talked about adopting Sophie, and about the other things that were important to him. Jim ended the call by asking if it would be okay with Michael if he stayed in touch, saying that his company regularly sponsored classes and events that might be of interest.

Michael told Jim that he should, "Absolutely keep in touch," and he meant it.

Jim's call, and the connection it created between the two men, got Michael thinking that it was time for him to resurrect his old database and create some connections of his own. The idea was a little daunting, but he knew just who to ask for help.

He picked up his phone and texted Mandi, asking if she still went to the dog park every Thursday. He continued, "I'd love to meet up and talk. I'm finally ready to make a change."

"Great to hear from you!" Mandi replied almost instantly. "I'm here to help you in any way I can. I'm sure Gizmo would love to see Sophie as well. We'll see you this Thursday at 2:30."

Chapter 6

Pump the Brakes

It was Thursday morning, and Michael was looking forward to seeing Mandi and Gizmo. He checked Mandi's social media page to see what she had been doing since he saw her in January. The photos she posted told the story. There were pictures of Mandi holding the trophy she was given for being the top-producing agent in her large office. There was an entire album full of photos from a trip she and her husband took to Egypt. As Michael stared at the images of them riding camels past the Great Pyramids, all he could think about was how amazing her life was, and how much he hoped to learn from her.

Michael got to the dog park about twenty minutes early so that Sophie could burn off a little steam and run with the other dogs before Gizmo and Mandi showed up. He remembered the expression, "A tired dog is a good dog," and was hoping it was true. By the time Mandi and Gizmo arrived, Sophie had worn herself out and was resting calmly at Michael's feet.

Gizmo heeled obediently as he and Mandi came through the gate. She unhooked his leash and released him into the play yard. She sat down on the bench next to Michael and noticed that Sophie seemed much calmer and more confident than she had been in January.

"How have things been going with Sophie?" Mandi asked.

Michael told her all about obedience training and what Sophie had been learning. Sophie even showed off some of her new tricks. Just as Michael was telling Mandi how proud he was of Sophie, she started jumping on him, competing with Mandi for his attention. But when Michael told her to "Sit," she obeyed right away and stayed until he released her. Mandi was impressed at how far both Michael and Sophie had come in the short time since they'd last seen each other.

The two dogs ran to the other side of the yard to play with a couple of Dachshunds that had just come through the gate. The four dogs were enjoying a game of chase, switching roles between being the chaser and the target. One Dachshund had a comical stop, drop, and roll move that he used to evade his chasers.

After watching the dogs for several minutes, Mandi said, "I was excited to get your text. Tell me what's been going on. Sounds like you might be ready to change the way you're doing business?"

Michael told Mandi about the different ways he had been trying to drum up business. He talked about resorting to using The Beast's tactics but admitted that it hadn't worked out well. He explained that business had picked up for him somewhat after he shifted to working "for sale by owners" and "geographic farming."

"Things were just going okay," he said, "Then I got this unexpected phone call from a guy named Jim Evans. We had this interesting conversation that made me realize I needed to reach out to you."

"Is Jim an old friend of yours?" Mandi asked.

"Actually, he said he met me at a class that his company-sponsored, but I don't remember anything about him. After our call, I looked through my phone for 'Jim Evans,' and I saw that I'd been getting emails from him every month for the past three years. He must have started emailing me right after the class. I hadn't bothered opening any of his emails, so I didn't recognize his name."

"So, you took a class with him, but hadn't talked to him for three years? And that reminded you of me? I'm confused."

"Exactly. I hadn't talked to this guy in three years, and in five minutes he managed to reconnect with me. It made me realize that maybe my database isn't hopeless. That was what made me contact you."

Mandi's eyes grew wide. "Got it! You want my help with reconnecting to your database. Well, you definitely came to the right place."

Michael talked to Mandi about that time during his first year in real estate when Gerri shared her "just be friends" method with him. He explained that he wasn't interested in doing that, because it felt inauthentic. He just wasn't *wired that way*.

Mandi reassured him, "It's not about having to be everybody's best friend, Michael. I can teach you some conversations that will work with who you are. Besides, the best gift you can offer your clients is your authentic self, not you pretending to be somebody else just to make a sale."

"You seem outgoing," Michael said. "With your personality, it must be easy to connect with people. For me, cold prospecting and sticking to business have always been easier."

Mandi took a deep breath and began, "Honestly, I started out cold prospecting, mostly out of necessity. My husband, Paul, was working eighty hours a week trying to keep his parents' little grocery store afloat after a big, new store had opened up nearby. It had a deli, a pharmacy, and a gas station. Our little store just couldn't compete. By the time Paul decided to close the business, we were deep in debt. We were desperate to find a solution. I had just gotten into real estate, and I happened to go to a training class on prospecting. I realized that if I could find just one FSBO or expired listing, I could convert it into a listing within a week and the money would start coming in. It worked for me, so I just ran with it."

She went on, "Prospecting gave me a certain...thrill of the hunt. I knew that when I called a FSBO or expired listing, I was reaching someone who had already decided to sell their home. Chasing those sellers was quick and easy, but I realized that chasing leads wasn't why I got into real estate. I wanted to help people. I wanted to be a trusted professional, not some lioness, hiding in the grass, waiting to pounce on her next meal."

Michael hung on every word. He asked Mandi what she had done to make the shift to driving her business through her database.

"Crazy enough, I was in another training class when our coach shared the NAR Home Buyer/Seller Survey. I was blown away to find out that most people choose their agent either because they already have a relationship with the agent or because they were referred to the agent. That was a huge wake-up call. I had gotten a few referrals by that point, but I wasn't being purposeful about cultivating referral business."

Mandi continued, "I started working with our coach one on one. The single most important thing I learned was a quote from Susan Scott, and that is, '**The conversation is the relationship.**' Once I understood this I was able to implement systems for attracting referrals and repeat business. I had to start having the conversations that built relationships with people that would ask me, trust me, and listen to me when it came to anything related to real estate."

Michael was eager to change his approach. "I'm ready to do this! Tell me what to say and I'll jam my database into a dialer and crank out the calls."

Mandi pumped the brakes. "Whoa! Hold on! Jamming contacts into a dialer and just powering through is not the way to do this. You don't jam anything. This is a process, and there's a system. I'll email you some scripts tonight to practice. Remember, your focus should be on adding value to the people on the other end of the line. This first week, I only want you to contact people in your database whose last name begins with the letters C&K. If you don't reach someone on the first or second try, call again in a few days. You need to make up to three attempts to call everyone on your list before we get together next week. Purposeful. I want you to be purposeful."

Steve Schlueter

Chapter 7

Cash Kow

Michael spent the weekend preparing his "C&K" call list. He was relieved to see that his database was better organized than he had expected. His former assistant had done a good job of cleaning up his entries and checking for completeness. He had addresses and emails for the majority of his contacts, and several of them had links to their social media profiles. He checked the unfamiliar names on his list against the Do Not Call Registry and tagged any matching names as "DNC" (do not call.)

Mandi had instructed Michael to not include his Internet leads in this call group. These calls were to focus solely on his sphere of influence and past clients. He remembered that Mandi had encouraged him to stay out of call bias by reaching out to everyone on the list, whether he remembered them or not. She gave him a script specifically written to take the dread out of making *those* calls.

"You might be surprised how easy it is to reconnect with some of those mystery contacts," Mandi had said. "Think about your call with Jim Evans. He reconnected with you in just a few minutes by showing interest in things that mattered to you."

On Monday morning he started making calls, beginning

with the most familiar names on the list. Those should have been the easiest calls to make, but he found himself feeling a little ashamed that he'd been out of touch for so long. After a few deep breaths, he tapped out that first phone number.

He was surprised that most people were happy to hear from him. He was even more surprised that he was enjoying reconnecting with people. The script that Mandi gave him didn't feel like a script at all. It felt like a conversation. It felt like something he could do.

Michael dialed the forty-seven people from his C&K group on Monday and had conversations with thirteen of those people. He followed Mandi's instructions and left a voicemail for the remaining thirty-four people, letting them know that he would reach out again later in the week.

***

On Wednesday morning, Michael woke up with a stuffy nose and headache. Was he catching a cold? Maybe it was his allergies? Either way, he just wanted to stay in bed.

After hitting the snooze button twice, Michael checked his phone and saw a text from Mandi: "Trust all is going well with your C&Ks. It's supposed to rain tomorrow, so no dog park. Good news, though! My coach said he could meet you on Friday at 1 p.m. Can you make it?"

Michael replied right away. "Friday at 1:00 is great, thanks! I'm just about to start on my calls."

Mandi seemed grateful to her coach for helping her transform her life and business. Michael hoped that his new relationship with Mandi and her coach would lead him to a transformation. He thought back to New Year's Day and his decision to make this a better year.

With a burst of enthusiasm, Michael hopped out of bed and

into the shower. The steam cleared his head, and he was ready to start making calls.

Michael's second-attempt calls were productive. He connected with another thirteen of the forty-seven contacts in his C&K group. More importantly, it led to some realizations.

He took a moment to do the math and calculated. He thought, *If I had just loaded everybody in a dialer and run through my list, I would've only connected with the thirteen people I reached on that first attempt, which is twenty-seven percent of that group. Today, by making the second attempt, I've talked to fifty-five percent of that group. I've got two leads that are looking to make a move in the next ninety days and one potential referral. If I hadn't made the second attempt, I wouldn't have gotten any of those opportunities. What was it that Mandi had said? 'The conversation is the relationship?' Heck, it's also the opportunity.*

Michael was thrilled that he had followed through even though he hadn't felt up to it. He found out that a good lead generation session was a powerful elixir for his troubles.

***

On Thursday afternoon, Michael was reluctant to make his calls. He looked for excuses to avoid them. The last two days of calling had been successful, but the conversations still felt awkward and unnatural. Michael knew that Mandi would follow up with him about how his calls had gone, and he certainly didn't want to have to admit to her that he had given up after his second attempt.

He rationalized, *I'll just get the first two out of the way. After the first two, the rest will be easier.*

Michael picked up his phone and started dialing. In ninety minutes, he managed to speak with nine of the people on his list. One of those nine conversations was with a Bill Kurtz. Even though he did not recognize the name, he followed Mandi's advice about not giving in to call bias, and made the call, using the "Mystery Person" script Mandi had provided.

As the conversation progressed, Michael realized that he had met Bill at an open house a couple of years earlier. Bill and his wife had been renting a home for the past two years and were ready to buy! Michael set an appointment with the Joneses for the following week.

After his third attempt, there were twelve people that Michael had not been able to reach. He followed up with that group by sending a quick text, writing, "Hi. It's Michael Barnes. Sorry I missed you this week. I was just checking in to see how you are. I'm here to serve your needs if you ever need anything. All the best."

That evening, Michael, to celebrate his week, cooked himself a nice steak dinner with all the trimmings. As he stood next to the grill watching the flames, he reflected on how much more intentional his week had felt. By focusing on just the C&K group, he was able to make his database calls and still have time to contact his FSBOs and knock on doors in his geographic farm. Maybe that's what Mandi meant by purposeful. He couldn't wait to learn more on Friday.

Chapter 8

Loyal Companion

Michael inched through the busy lunchtime traffic to Mandi's office feeling anxious and uncertain about meeting this coach. He still worried that because he wasn't naturally social or interested in "making friends" with his clients, Mandi's system wasn't right for him. He let out a sigh as he parked his car.

Mandi, seeing Michael pull into the parking lot, hurried to the front desk to welcome him.

"Michael, you're right on time. Coach is eager to see you."

As they walked down the hall to Victor's office, Mandi invited Michael to pop into her office when he finished his meeting.

Victor and Michael settled in to get acquainted. Victor could sense that Michael was uneasy, so he opened the conversation by asking Michael about his background and his career in real estate. He wanted to get a better understanding of Michael's strengths, weaknesses, and opportunities for growth.

Victor surprised Michael by asking about the call he got from Jim Evans. "Mandi said that Jim's phone call is what spurred you into action. Tell me more about that."

Michael told Victor about Jim's call, and how it had left him with an unexpected sense of connection. Jim's call had caused him to rethink how he was connecting with his clients. He told Victor how he had searched through his phone for Jim's name after the call, only to discover that he had been getting emails from Jim for years without realizing it. Those emails had gone unopened, but that one call changed the nature of the relationship.

"I'm curious," Victor said. "Did you get that call from Jim the week of April 12?"

Michael was caught off guard by the question. "Yeah, it was that week, actually. How did you know that?"

"Well, Jim is a new client of mine, and, in early April, he and I were working on ways he could reach his database. I'm the one who told him that week to make reconnection calls with those in his database whose last names start with B&E. I am interested to hear how the call went, from your perspective. Can you remember any specific questions Jim asked you?"

"Yeah, some of them, which is strange, because I usually can't even remember what I ate for breakfast."

They went over a few of the questions Jim had asked, and how Michael felt about them. As Michael shared his experience, he realized that the conversation he was having with Victor gave him the same feeling of connection that he had felt with Jim. Victor's warmth and openness put Michael at ease.

Victor said, "The reason you remember your conversation with Jim is because he asked his questions using the F.O.R.D. method. **F**amily (or **F**riends), **O**ccupation, **R**ecreation, and **D**reams. Those four subjects, posed as questions, are the secret to having meaningful conversations with people."

Victor reached into his desk, pulled out a sheet of sample F.O.R.D. questions, and handed it to Michael.

"Let's try something, shall we? Take a look at those questions I just gave you. Now imagine we're at a Board of

Realtors luncheon, and Mandi has just introduced us. I want you to get to know me by asking me a F.O.R.D. question from each category. Listen carefully to my response to each one and ask an appropriate follow-up question. Remember, you don't need to ask F.O.R.D. questions in order. As a matter of fact, it's sometimes easier to start with Occupation questions when meeting someone for the first time."

Michael studied the questions, and started by asking Victor, "What did you do before real estate?"

"I went to university in Mexico City and got my degree in psychology. Then I worked at a clinic for a few years after graduation. But I soon realized I would need an advanced degree to go into practice in the U.S. I was getting married and couldn't afford to go back to school, so I became a real estate agent instead."

"Wow", Michael said, "That's quite a journey! What made you get into coaching?"

"Well, after a few years in real estate, I noticed that many agents were falling short of their potential. They would come to me for help, and in most cases, it was their thinking that was holding them back. Many people struggle with limiting beliefs. They think they're not good enough or don't have what it takes to be successful. My psychology background allowed me to help agents reframe their thinking. After that, we were able to identify the skills and systems to help them move forward."

Michael asked Victor why he had chosen to go to college in Mexico City.

"I was born there", Victor explained. "Growing up, my family would spend time in both Mexico and the United States. When it was time for college, I wanted to be in Mexico, where my friends were. I was lucky I stayed because I met my wife Julie when she came to my university for a study-abroad program."

Michael asked, "Do you and Julie have children?"

"Yes, we have two. Amy is fifteen and Roland is thirteen. Amy is our volleyball player, and Roland plays baseball. They keep us busy."

"You're a lucky man, Victor. It sounds like you have a wonderful family."

Coach complimented Michael on his level of engagement and his follow-up questions. He then prompted Michael to continue with questions for **Recreation** and **Dreams**. He reinforced the importance of carefully listening to his responses and told Michael to trust his intuition for the appropriate follow-up question.

"Stay in curiosity," he said.

Michael then moved to **Recreation**, "So, Victor, how do you spend your free time?"

Victor glanced out the window toward the parking lot and said, "You see that big pickup? That's my tow rig. We've got a big fifth-wheel trailer we call the 'Starship Enterprise.' We like to pack up the family and go discover the country. We've been working our way through the national parks."

Michael followed up with, "Which park is your favorite, so far?"

"I'd have to say Yellowstone is our favorite so far. We spent two incredible weeks there, watching the wildlife and exploring the geothermal features. The kids were amazed to learn about the huge volcano, and Julie and I loved the waterfalls. There was no TV or cell service in the park, so we had some great family bonding time."

Michael transitioned into his **Dreams** question by asking, "Yellowstone sounds awesome! Where would you go next, if you could plan the perfect trip?"

"Well, now that the kids are a little older, we'd like to take them to Europe. We want to expose them to its rich history and culture. That's the next big thing on our family bucket list."

"Which countries would you visit first?"

"We want to start in Italy, see the ruins in Rome and Pompeii, and the Greek temples in Paestum," Victor replied.

"Wow. Sounds like the trip of a lifetime," Michael said, wrapping up his questions.

Victor leaned back in his chair and said, "Michael, there's still a lot you don't know about me, but just look at how much you do know! More importantly, I feel more connected to you because you've shown interest in me, and you have greater insight into who I am and what I value." He sat back in his chair. "I'm curious, how did it feel for you to use the F.O.R.D. method? Do you think it's a technique that you'd feel comfortable putting into practice?"

"The sample questions helped get me started", Michael answered. "It still felt a little forced, because I'm not naturally social, but I think it's something I can learn to do. I'm ready to learn more about the systems you've taught Mandi."

"Michael, F.O.R.D. conversations are one of the five foundational principles that I teach agents who want to build a relationship-based business. I'm willing to share these with you, at no charge, on one condition. For you to internalize these principles, I'm going to ask that you follow through one hundred percent on the homework I give you. These first principles will help prepare you for my advanced coaching group. Are you willing to commit to completing the assignments as a condition of continuing with the first five sessions?"

Michael was honored by Victor's offer and agreed to do his part.

"So, what's my first assignment?" Michael asked.

Victor responded, "Last week, Mandi had you call the people in your database whose names begin with C&K. That was part of principle number two, called **'Doing the Database Two'** or

'DTD2,' for short. This coming week, I want you to contact people whose last names begin with F&G. Your goal is to blend some F.O.R.D. questions into your business conversations during these calls. You'll notice that the scripts Mandi sent you are designed this way. In the advanced coaching sessions, we cover more detailed techniques for structuring these blended conversations. For now, just use the engagement questions we've built for you."

Michael stopped by Mandi's office on his way out.

Mandi smiled, "So, how'd it go?"

"Fantastic! We worked on F.O.R.D. questions today, and I got to know Victor a little better. He offered to take me through these first five sessions, as long as I do my homework."

"In that case, you'd better do the homework! I remember when Victor had me practice the F.O.R.D. questions on him. That was how I found out about Chico, his Chiweenie. We talked a lot about our rescue dogs. We even gave the five principles dog-related nicknames to help me remember them."

"'Dog-related nicknames?'" Michael asked as he raised an eyebrow.

"Yeah! Think about it! F.O.R.D. conversations help us to be perceived as **Loyal Companions**. We are there when our clients need us, just like our furry friends are there for us when we need them. Next week's theme will be **Flea and Tick Prevention**."

"Flea and what?"

Mandi got an urgent phone call before Michael got an explanation. She looked up at Michael and whispered, "See you on Thursday!"

Chapter 9

Be Prepared

On Monday, Michael started in on his F&G calls. He worked hard to be consistent about calling his database and honoring his commitment to Victor. For the most part, he was feeling energized about his business and the direction it was headed. Yet, on Wednesday, The Beast got under his skin.

Michael gave up his private office when his business slowed down, so he had been working in an open cubicle area near the other agents. Chris overheard Michael having F.O.R.D. conversations with his database and wandered over to his desk with a smirk.

"Dude, stop being so weird. People don't want to answer those goofy questions."

"Here. Take these," The Beast said, handing Michael a sheet of paper.

"What's this?" Michael asked, annoyed by Chris's attitude.

"Just a few Internet leads. It's a beautiful day, and I'm going golfing. I don't have time to make any more calls before tee time. Why don't you get on that phone of yours, and smile and dial? That's the way to make money."

"I'm good, thanks," Michael said, imagining giving Chris

the finger.

Deep down, Michael knew he was on the right path with Victor but needed Mandi's reassurance. He was looking forward to seeing her and Gizmo at the dog park on Thursday.

Michael took Sophie to the park a little early, hoping to spend some time working on her new roll-over trick. He got her to do it a couple of times but found himself getting frustrated because she was so distracted by the other dogs. He thought about it for a minute and realized that when he was working on a new skill, like scripts, he needed to be in a quiet place where he could concentrate. It wasn't fair for him to expect Sophie to focus on her new skills in a place with so many distractions. He had been so eager to impress Mandi with Sophie's new tricks that he had forgotten about what was best for Sophie.

Just then, Mandi led Gizmo through the gate and into the small dog area. Sophie spotted them immediately. The two dogs greeted each other with a sniff and ran off to play.

Right away, Mandi asked, "So how did it go this week? I want to hear all about it."

Michael explained that he finished all of the assignments Victor had given him. He had thirty-five people in his DTD2 group and was able to speak to twenty-seven of them by using the three-attempt approach.

"Surprisingly, nobody was rude, and people were generally happy to hear from me. The F.O.R.D. questions, along with Victor's business conversation scripts, helped me connect with people."

"That's fantastic," Mandi said. "Did you run into any problems?"

"I did have one call that I was not prepared for. I called Jeff, an old friend that I hadn't spoken to in a few years. He mentioned that his wife had a routine surgical procedure, ended up getting an infection, and passed away unexpectedly. I could hear that his heart was broken, and he was a little lost. I let him talk for as long as he needed. When he finished, he thanked me for calling, and for offering my support. We are meeting soon for coffee. I'm glad we reconnected, but the call got pretty uncomfortable for me. I was worried I wouldn't know what to say to him."

"Poor Jeff. What awful news," Mandi responded. She sat quietly for a moment and then asked, "What is the worst response you can imagine to the question of how work is going?"

Michael answered, "They might say that they got laid off and were having trouble finding a new job."

"Ok. If someone says they've lost their job, I respond empathetically with, 'I'm so sorry to hear that. I've got a lot of connections in my network; do you have a resume?' If they do, I'd invite them to share it with me, and say, 'If I learn about an opportunity for you, I'm happy to pass your resume along.' You can even go a step further and ask them to describe their perfect next job. That way you're *future pacing* them toward a solution, instead of getting caught up in being sorry for them. That will foster positivity."

"Tell me what you might say if someone tells you they got a promotion and a big bump in salary?" Mandi then asked.

"I guess I could say 'Wow, congratulations! You must be excited. What does a promotion like this mean for your family, and your lifestyle?"

"That's perfect!" Mandi said. "In that case, make sure you follow up with them more often. A windfall like that could be a marker for change. In fact, if you listen closely during your F.O.R.D. conversations, you'll often hear indicators of upcoming changes. Maybe your client hasn't decided to do something with their real estate situation yet, but major life changes can trigger a real estate transaction. Take note of these indicators and cultivate those relationships by placing them in your database as a person to *nurture* with more frequent contact.

As Michael thought back on the details of a few of his calls, he realized he could identify two contacts that fit into the "nurture" category. They both had life situations that made them highly likely to buy or sell real estate in the next twelve months.

There was a client who told him that their youngest child was about to leave for college out of state. Michael decided to put them on a more frequent follow-up plan, so he would know when they decided to make a move. He also spoke with someone who was offered a job in another town and needed some information on housing costs that they could use as part of their salary negotiation. A move across the state would mean that his clients would have a house to sell, making it a definite "nurture."

Another challenge Michael shared with Mandi was the handful of calls that seemed to take way too long. They were good calls, and yet they slowed down his progress and derailed his momentum.

Mandi commiserated, "This is something that DTD2 helps with. I've got a special tag I use for chatty people. I call them at the end of the day, so I don't lose momentum. Other times, I open the call with, 'Hey, I saw that I had ten minutes before my next appointment, so I wanted to check in. I've been thinking about you.'"

Mandi continued, "If you have chatty people who are real advocates, make sure to allow more time for their call at least once a year. I usually do that in the fourth quarter, because I've found that the conversations and events we do in the fourth quarter are the seeds for my first-quarter business. Lots of agents slow down in the fourth quarter, not realizing that there's plenty of business to be had at the end of the year. Last year, the fourth quarter was my second busiest time, coming in just short of the second quarter. Try not to let yourself get distracted with the holidays or neglect your database during Q4, or you'll pay for it in Q1 of the following year."

Michael looked up at Mandi. "You sure put a lot of faith in DTD2. Are you sure it's the best way to do this? This week I only had thirty-five people on my F&G contact list. I had time to make more calls than that. Why wouldn't I just keep going, and work through the rest of my contacts?"

Mandi smiled, "Well, you could do that. But, let me ask you a question. How did it feel today when you wrapped up your calls, knowing that you'd completed the most important activity for the week?"

"It felt great," Michael answered.

"If that's the feeling you'd like to have as you work through your database, even as you expand it, just trust the system. Coach and I call this part **Flea and Tick Prevention**. Just like we give Sophie and Gizmo their flea and tick treatment regularly, DTD2 is like flea and tick prevention for our database."

"What does that even mean, flea and tick prevention? You mentioned that last week. What are you talking about?"

"Coach can explain the dog analogies to you tomorrow. He put things in a context that helped me understand how much was at stake for my business and our industry. Let's just say that I now protect my database from invaders just like I protect Gizmo from invaders."

Steve Schlueter

Chapter 10

Flea and Tick Prevention

On Friday, Coach kicked off his meeting by asking about Michael's plans for the upcoming weekend.

Michael said, "Sunday is supposed to be a beautiful day, so I plan to take Sophie out to the Canyons Nature Preserve to hike the trails. It will be her first time hiking, and I think she'll have a great time chasing the chipmunks."

Michael had never loved hiking, but since Tonya enjoyed it, he'd been to the canyons with her a few times. What he didn't tell Victor was that he was secretly hoping he would bump into Tonya. He hadn't seen or spoken to her in six months, and she'd been on his mind a lot recently.

Michael caught his mind drifting, and refocused his attention on Victor, who had shifted the conversation to business.

"Before we get started on principle number two, do you have any questions for me?"

"I do, actually. Mandi said something about 'flea and tick prevention.' How does that relate to my real estate business?"

Coach explained, "Well, think about it this way, Michael. If you don't give Sophie preventative treatments, she would be susceptible to fleas and ticks. Once she got them, they would end up infesting your entire home."

"That's...disgusting," Michael said. "But I still don't see how this relates to business."

Victor continued, "Fleas and ticks are opportunistic. They're just waiting to find an animal whose owner has neglected to care for them properly, so they can move in. Fleas and ticks are a metaphor for your competition. If you don't properly care for your clients, you can be sure that some opportunistic competitor, real estate portal, or iBuyer is out there waiting for a chance to latch on to them."

Michael certainly didn't want his competition latching on to his clients. "How do I keep the 'fleas and ticks' away from my database?"

"It's simple, Michael. Well, it's simple, but not easy. Defending your database against fleas and ticks involves **communicating** with your connected contacts **regularly** and **systematically**, in a way that **adds value** to those relationships."

Michael asked for clarification on the difference between a **database contact** and a **connected contact**.

Victor explained that a connected contact was someone with whom you have had actual two-way communication, either in person or by phone. "Internet leads that you've never spoken with," he clarified, "are not considered connected contacts in the DTD2 system."

"The conversations are the critical components," he continued. "You may not have realized it, but you've been using DTD2 for two weeks now. Did you follow through on your commitment to making your calls last week, using the three-attempt approach?"

"Absolutely, Coach. I did everything you asked me to do."

"Excellent! How did things go?"

Michael shared that he was having more conversations and

felt good about the idea of having a beginning and end to each week. On Thursday, when he wrapped up his database calls, he knew that he'd completed his most important work for the week.

"Great takeaway! You're developing a powerful habit by sticking to the routine. What else has happened in the last two weeks?"

"Well, I found myself having conversations with people whose names I didn't recognize. Up until now, I probably would've skipped calling those people because I wouldn't know what to say to them. I ended up adding a couple of things to my pipeline because Mandi told me to not shy away from my 'mystery contacts.'"

"Are you willing to maintain that posture every week, staying out of call bias, and trusting the system?" Coach asked.

"I am. I can already feel things starting to change for me, and I want to stick with it and see where it takes me," replied Michael.

"I don't know if Mandi mentioned this to you, but it's okay if you decide to eliminate a contact after you've had a call with them. If you find that someone is not a good match, or if you come across someone rude or angry, you have the absolute right to remove that person. But until you remove a contact, you need to commit to calling them."

"Got it, Coach. Hopefully, I won't have to delete too many names."

"Remember, these calls are all about value and contribution. As you get better at this, you'll rarely experience anything that feels like rejection. Once people know that you are there to serve them, they'll be happy to hear from you," Coach shared.

Michael began to look ahead.

He asked Victor, "What do I do when my database gets

massive? If it gets bigger, and I get super busy, how do I keep up with it?"

"That's a great question, Michael. We have mega agent teams selling over $100,000,000 a year using this system. It's completely scalable. We'll talk more about that as you grow.

"For now, I have two assignments for you," Coach continued. "This week, I want you to contact your M&X group. Keep using F.O.R.D. questions, blended with business conversations, and focus on adding value. You probably don't have a lot of contacts whose name begins with X, so I'm also asking that you **integrate DTD2 into your social media strategy**. I'll send you an email with a tutorial on how to tie your social media accounts into the system. It's helpful to create custom friends lists, divided by two-letter groups. This will allow you to target a specific group with a specific message the week before you call them. Another way to use your social-media friends lists is to read the posts only from that week's letter group and comment, like, or share the content. Interacting with their posts the week before your call will give you topics for engaging F.O.R.D. questions."

As their session came to a close, Michael thanked Coach for his time and promised to concentrate on his flea and tick prevention strategies.

Chapter 11

Oh, Behave!

Michael's coaching session with Victor motivated him to do his homework. He began by watching the social media tutorial that Victor had sent, but he spent way too much time creating his social-media friends lists. In hindsight, he should have broken that project down into thirteen smaller projects.

He completed his DTD2 calls and stuck to the three-attempt approach. Even though his calls went well, and he was generating good leads, he was still not completely comfortable with the F.O.R.D. conversations. He still felt insincere. He cared about people, yet this was stressful. He kept having flashbacks to his coworker, Gerri, and her comment about needing to be friends with all of his clients. The F.O.R.D. method was making it easier for him to have conversations, but he still had his doubts about his ability to connect with people.

To make matters worse, The Beast was back in his face again this week, handing him leads, pushing him, "Hey, are you still using those dumb scripts? Don't waste time on that stuff."

Michael pushed back. He told Chris about the success he'd been having. He'd gotten leads he was nurturing and had set several appointments.

Chris sniped, "Hey, it's your funeral, dude."

"Just wait and see. I'll be hot on your tail by the end of the year!" Michael answered.

Michael was proud of how he handled Chris. He resolved to lean into his activities more intentionally, and now he had something to prove.

Michael remembered what Mandi had said to him after his last face-off with Chris.

She had said, "He has a wake-up call coming. You can't buy enough leads to sustain a successful business long term. You must develop your relationships."

He could just look at Mandi's career and know she was right, but the relationship piece still didn't feel natural to him.

Michael was looking forward to seeing Mandi. He hoped she could help him adjust his mindset. It was still easier for him to make calls to *for sale by owners*, even though that segment of the market was extremely competitive and yielded mediocre results. He was more comfortable having strictly business conversations, which is what he could do with the FSBOs.

***

Michael stopped by the coffee shop on his way to the dog park and picked up two lattes and some puppuccinos. The espresso machines whooshed. Customers chatted around him as he waited for his order. Standing at the counter, he thought about how grateful he felt to have Coach and Mandi in his life. He appreciated how they met him where he was, without judging him. He could tell they wanted to help him succeed. He tried to focus on staying in gratitude.

Later on, at the park, Michael opened up to Mandi about being uncomfortable making his database calls. "I want to grow my business, but I have to force myself to make my calls. I'm just not a **people person**. Honestly, if I didn't have you and Coach keeping me accountable, I don't know if I would be sticking with it right now."

Mandi assured him that what he was feeling was completely natural. She talked with him about Gary Keller's book, *The One Thing*, and how it takes around 66 days to instill a new habit. She encouraged him to keep pushing forward because it had only been a few weeks since he started using DTD2.

She explained that, in time, it would get easier and more natural for him and that the struggle is part of the lesson.

"The activities," she explained, "help you flesh out the beliefs that can get in your way. You need to reframe your **thinking** to support your **doing**. Right now, you're relying on willpower to keep **doing**, which is part of why you're struggling. The other factor to consider is your **natural behavioral style**."

"My natural behavioral style?" Michael asked.

"Yep. Think of it this way, are you taking Sophie to obedience school to make her a Rottweiler?"

"What? I'm not sure I'm following you."

"Are you trying to turn your dog into another breed, one with a different core behavior?" she asked.

"That's not even possible! She's a Miniature Manchester Terrier, which is exactly what she was meant to be," Michael replied.

"So, why are you taking her to obedience school then?"

"Well, she needs to learn certain commands and skills to be safe and well behaved. I want to be able to take her out with me more and have her be calm around people and other dogs."

"No matter how much you train her, you'll never take the terrier out of her. Sure, you can train her to respond to commands, but if you're out on a walk and she sees a squirrel, isn't her first instinct going to be to chase that squirrel?"

"Yeah, she's going to want to run after it. The commands help her with impulse control, but she still makes that little prey squeal, because it's just part of who she is."

"So, what I'm hearing you say is that Sophie is learning to modify her natural behavior through obedience training, and her modified behavior enhances the experience that you have with her, right? It sounds like you can take her more places than you used to because she's better behaved. Yet she's still herself, isn't she?" Mandi asked.

"Yes, she is still her Mini Manchester self," Michael said as the light bulb went off in his head. "Sounds like I may need to go to **obedience school** for wayward real estate agents, so I can learn to be successful while staying true to myself."

"Funny you should say that. **Obedience School** is my nickname for your next lesson," Mandi chuckled.

Chapter 12

Obedience School

As Michael pulled into the parking lot at Coach's office, he noticed Victor's fifth-wheel camper attached to his pickup. It had a rack of bicycles at the rear and looked ready for travel. The rig looked like the perfect home away from home.

He walked in, saw Coach, and remarked, "Looks like you're taking the Enterprise on another adventure! Where are you and the family headed?"

Coach shared that he was taking the family to Garner State Park. It was their favorite place to be this time of year because the crawdads were out. The kids loved to catch crawdads! He explained that the kids had three days off school the following week, and he and his wife had decided to take them out of class for an extra two days and make a vacation of it. Michael was eager to learn more about the park and thought he might like to take Sophie one weekend.

The men spent time talking about Michael's progress. Coach was impressed that Michael had gotten all his activities done and was excited to learn that his efforts were paying off. He sensed Michael was holding back and asked about any challenges he may have encountered.

Michael admitted, "F.O.R.D. and the scripts are helping for sure, but I still feel like I'm supposed to be everybody's best friend, and it makes me uncomfortable. I have to force myself to start my calls. Mandi said that I should focus on being their trusted advisor, but I guess I don't know how that exactly looks. She also talked about **Obedience School**, which is where I'm apparently headed today?"

"Well, Michael, with dogs, their breed influences their behavior. Scientific studies have shown that many dog behaviors like trainability and stranger aggression are linked to genetics. We're no different. We all have our behavioral preferences based on our programming, experiences, and upbringing. What about you? Have you ever taken a behavioral assessment?"

"I have, but it was a long time ago. I was told I was a high dominant, or a 'High D,' but I've never completely understood how that impacts my daily life."

"It sounds like you took a DISC behavioral assessment," Coach said. "Behavior is a fascinating study, particularly in learning to understand ourselves and how we relate to others. We just have to be careful not to put ourselves in a box by thinking that we can't do something because we are—or aren't—a certain behavioral style.

"It's important," Coach continued, "that you connect with people in a way that is authentically you. Different approaches fit with each behavioral style. You've already experienced the stress of making calls in a way that was not entirely suited to your behavioral DNA. Today, I'd like to help you learn to add value to your relationships while working within your natural behavioral style."

"I'd like that. I don't want to keep trying to be everyone's best friend on these calls. I'm not one of these social people who can just talk to everyone like they're an old friend."

"Let's not assume that everyone who's naturally social has an easy time connecting with their database. It might seem that way to you, but social people fear rejection, so they tend to avoid the business aspects of conversations. Every behavioral style has its challenges when it comes to doing the work. Limiting beliefs get in the way of success."

Coach continued, "You said you were identified as a 'High D,' or driver. This behavioral style is task-oriented and wired for achievement. You like to get things done and may even be a little impatient. High D's can be uncomfortable with small talk, chitchat, and anything that slows them down. You may not be strongly wired for relationships, but that's okay. Next week, try treating your DTD2 calls as a task that needs to be completed. You can also focus on the accomplishments that come from your efforts. You don't need to be infinitely adjustable in your behavior, but you do need to adopt a strategy that allows you to be authentic."

Coach leaned forward and said, "I know that Mandi passed along some scripts, and you've been working with your F.O.R.D. conversations. Now let's talk more about being the **Trusted Advisor** for the folks in your database."

"I've never really thought of myself as an **advisor**," Michael said.

"Let's say that you had your entire retirement savings in an IRA, and your financial advisor called you once a quarter to update you on market trends and offer support. How would you feel about that? Would that offend you?"

"No, I would probably be impressed that they were actually paying attention to my needs and sharing their insights with me," Michael replied.

"Exactly! Your role is to help your clients make decisions about what is likely their largest asset, which is their home. If you were in the role of trusted advisor, what factors would you say are impacting your clients right now? You need to build your conversations around the answers to that question."

Michael thought for a moment, and then said, "Well, my first thought is the low-interest rates and whether they've refinanced."

"Okay, that's a good one. What else?" Victor asked.

"It's tax assessment time. Are they being properly assessed, or are they paying too much in taxes? I could even invite them to a seminar on real estate investing."

"Being the Trusted Advisor doesn't have to be just about real estate. You can be a resource for contractors and other service professionals. We'll talk more about that in two weeks, when we discuss principle four, building your **Business Referral Network**. It's okay to place more energy on the **Trusted Advisor** portion of the call, but elements of F.O.R.D. have to be a part of the conversation. This is something we work to master in the advanced coaching group. In the meantime, just follow the flow of the scripts and don't skip the relationship-building questions."

They were out of time, so Coach gave Michael his next assignment. "Stay on your DTD2 contacts for the next two weeks. I'd like you to keep a journal about your lead generation, particularly your thoughts around establishing yourself as a trusted advisor. Make notes each day of how authentic you feel, and how you feel your conversations went on a scale of 1-10. Make it a goal to improve your rating each day until you start consistently rating them in the 8-10 range. If you take the time to evaluate and make small adjustments in your approach, you will start having stronger conversations."

As Michael headed out to his car, he noticed a voicemail from Jim Evans. Jim had called to remind him that the charity car show was the next day and hoped Michael would be able to make it.

Chapter 13

California Windfall

On Saturday morning, Michael met his old friend Jeff Fischer at the new French bakery near Jeff's office. They had fun catching up and talking about old times.

Michael was blown away when Jeff apologized for not staying in touch. He said he'd been so busy with his career that he hadn't taken time to keep up with his old buddies. Michael knew *he*, too, felt guilty about not contacting his old friends, but it hadn't occurred to him that *they* might feel bad about not staying in touch with *him*.

A lot had happened in the four years since Michael and Jeff had last connected. The little tech company that Jeff joined when it was just a startup was thriving in its small AI niche. Jeff worked his way up the ranks and was now the COO of the company. The company was in the process of consolidating its small branch office in San Diego with its local office.

It appeared Jeff was doing well, at least financially, and Michael congratulated him on his success.

Jeff shared that it had been hard to be excited about his success since his wife's passing. He had worked hard to build a future for the two of them, but now that she was gone, he had to rethink everything. Michael sympathized and asked Jeff what he could do to support him.

Jeff appreciated Michael listening, and replied, "Honestly, just being here is a big help. This branch consolidation is keeping me distracted, for now. I'm going to take a trip back east to spend some time with my folks once it's completed."

Jeff mentioned that seven families in the San Diego branch were moving to the local office. Later that day, he and his assistant would be working on sending out their relocation offers.

He asked if Michael might be available to help his people with their home purchases. Michael appreciated the opportunity and assured Jeff that he would help with any need that might arise.

Jeff agreed to email Michael their contact information when he got back to the office, and Michael promised that he would check in with those folks on Sunday afternoon since they would all be getting their relocation packages by the end of the day Saturday.

"They're already kind of prepared for this," he said. "They'll probably want to start house hunting over the next couple of weeks. We're hoping to have everybody moved in within 60 to 90 days."

Michael promised he would contact everyone on Sunday and keep Jeff in the loop. They finished their coffee and agreed to get together again once the relocation project was wrapped up.

After the meeting, Michael was so energized about his new opportunity that he wanted to celebrate. He would go to the charity car show, after all. He stopped by the house to pick up Sophie, outfitted her with a leash and harness, and headed out.

***

The number of cars at the show amazed Michael. This was a much bigger event than he expected. Not having any idea what Jim looked like, Michael looked back on Jim's email, hoping to find a photo of him so he would know him when he saw him.

He stopped at the check-in desk to ask about Jim, and the attendant pointed him to a booth at the far right of the lot. He and Sophie took their time getting to Jim's booth. Seeing all these gorgeous cars got Michael thinking about getting his Chevelle out of storage.

Michael approached Jim's booth, and the men spent a few minutes chatting. Jim offered Sophie a dog treat, and they became fast friends.

Michael looked up and noticed that Jim's booth was directly across from a whole row of Ford Mustangs.

He commented, "Funny that you're here with all these Fords. I've started coaching with Victor, and he's been teaching me the principles of his system. It was the F.O.R.D. conversation with you that led me to contact Mandi, who connected me with Victor. I owe you a big thank you. Working with Victor has set my business on a whole new path."

"You're very welcome," Jim replied. "I'm thrilled it's working out for you. Victor mentioned you two had started working together. So, what's happened so far?"

Michael shared, "I had a big win this morning. I was doing my calls earlier this month, and I reconnected with an old friend. We hadn't been in touch for a few years. He's moved into an executive position at a small company, and he's got seven families relocating from California in the next several weeks. He's asked me to help them find their new homes. It's a direct result of doing DTD2 and staying out of call bias."

He continued, "If your call hadn't spurred me into taking action with my database, that would not have happened. So, thank you!"

Jim gave Michael a high five and said, "That's fantastic! I didn't know I did all that. Congratulations. Did you say that these folks are coming from California?"

"Yes, from the San Diego area."

"We've got a mortgage program for relocating families that allows them to count the trailing spouse's income for qualifying. That's often a challenge for buyers where one person's getting transferred and the other one is having to quit their job to move across the country. It might be a great option for some of those clients."

Michael thanked Jim for the tip and commented, "I don't know if my usual lender has that option. I've never heard him talk about it. Jim, since you're indirectly responsible for all of this, I want you to do the loans for these seven families."

Michael shared that he'd be talking to his new clients over the weekend and that Jim should be on the lookout for a call from him either Sunday afternoon or Monday.

Jim smiled and said, "Thanks so much. I was not expecting this to happen today! I promise to take exceptional care of your people. Now, let's go check out the cars. I saw a whole section of Chevelles on my way in."

Chapter 14

The Confession

Michael spent Sunday preparing for the week ahead, making sure he had his N&R call list in order.

He'd contacted all seven families from California, and four of them had already scheduled their house-hunting trips. One family was so eager to get started that they scheduled an appointment for Thursday, meaning he'd miss seeing Mandi at the dog park.

He hated to have to cancel, but this was a big opportunity. It had to be a priority, especially after discovering that all of these purchases were going to be in the $550,000 to $750,000 price range. Since this was well above average for his area, there were still a variety of good homes available.

As he planned his week, he saw he had two buyer consultations scheduled and three listing presentations, all from the work he'd done over the last few weeks. One listing appointment was a FSBO, and all his other opportunities were from working his DTD2s.

On Monday morning, Michael jumped right into his calls. He was intentional about using the **Trusted Advisor** approach and staying authentic. It seemed to work. He secured three nurtures for follow-up and one listing appointment. He also generated two buyer referrals that were planning to purchase new homes in the next six months or so. He referred those people to Jim to get pre-qualified and approved.

Michael ventured out to pick up some lunch and realized that his tired Chevy Tahoe was still having service issues. With the number of appointments he'd been setting, he felt more confident about the direction of his career and was ready to move up to a more dependable vehicle. He called one of his past clients, who worked at the local GMC dealership, and asked if he had any low-mileage SUVs.

He wasn't ready to commit to the big-ticket Cadillac Escalade he wanted. He decided he would take that plunge at the end of the year after he passed up The Beast. His friend at the dealership just happened to have a midnight blue GMC Yukon with only 42,000 miles on it. It was a pristine, one-owner SUV that had always been garaged. Driving away from the dealership, Michael felt proud.

***

Michael was back in the office the following Monday, and, for once, was looking forward to seeing The Beast. He walked confidently up to the sales board and posted two sales from his California buyers, his FSBO listing that went under contract Sunday, and a listing from his geo farm. He posted $2.3MM in pending sales just over the last few days.

As he stood at the sales board, celebrating his success, The Beast walked by and said, "Impressive. Someone's on a roll."

Michael turned and flashed a grin back at The Beast and said, "I'm coming for you!"

"Challenge accepted!"

Chris didn't show it, but he was impressed with the results of Michael, who was right on his heels.

***

Thursday rolled around, and it was finally time for another dog park outing with Mandi. Michael was eager to show off Sophie's latest trick, called, "Leave it." Michael would set down a treat and hold a second one in his hand. To get the treat in his hand, she had to leave the first one alone. Michael put down a treat and told Sophie to "Leave it." Sophie remained in the sitting position waiting to get the reward, but Gizmo ran over and stole the first treat from the ground.

Mandi said, "Oops, Gizmo hasn't learned that one. He's sorry, Sophie," patting Sophie on the head. Michael gave Sophie another treat and then the two dogs ran off to play.

Michael told Mandi about all the success he'd been having at work. She congratulated him and asked how he was feeling about things. He shared that he'd never felt better about the direction of his career but was not as optimistic about his personal life.

He told Mandi about his breakup with Tonya and admitted that his devotion to his work had contributed to their problems. He didn't want that to happen again.

Mandi asked, "Are you and Tonya still speaking?"

"No."

Michael told Mandi about Tonya's birthday, and how he had disappointed her for the last time.

He continued, "The way I acted on her birthday was the final blow for her, but the problem was bigger than just that one day. Looking back, I realize my life was out of control. I wasn't worthy of her."

"I can see why she felt undervalued, but do you think she did anything to make you feel unworthy?" Mandi asked.

"Actually, no," Michael said after some reflection. "That was my own insecurity. She was always kind and patient with me, even when I disappointed her. I felt guilty about hurting her feelings, which made me feel even less deserving of her. It was a cycle of self-sabotage."

Mandi said, "Maybe there's still hope for you and Tonya. People's reactions are not always their responses. Tonya was with you for a reason. She was attracted to something. I would encourage you to reflect on that. Think about the hopes and dreams she shared with you during your relationship. It sounds like your values may have been out of alignment when you split up."

Mandi shared that relationships can be challenging and that she and Paul had to learn to manage the demands of kids and careers while remaining connected as a couple. They adopted some rituals for strengthening their relationship after attending a couple's retreat. Each October, she explained, Victor would bring in a relationship expert to work with realtors and their spouses or partners. For her, one of the most helpful lessons ended up being a goal-setting exercise they learned, one she went on to describe.

"When it came to my work, I was accustomed to setting specific goals and plans for meeting them, but, as a couple, we were just winging it. Our life functions better now that we've put rituals in place to nurture our relationship. We're closer than we've ever been. Paul and I spend an hour each Sunday afternoon going over our family's schedules for the week. We make sure we are both dialed into the biggest priorities, and that we don't have any major scheduling conflicts. Thursday night is always date night, and we take turns planning the dates.

We either share the plan for date night on Sunday, so it gives us something to look forward to, or save it as a surprise when it's something unique."

Mandi continued, "Another thing that has helped was committing to taking Sundays off to be with my family. We have this saying at our company, 'The purpose of business is to fund your truly perfect life.' For me, that means that real estate doesn't have to be my entire life. It's there to fund those things that are truly important to my family and me. I suggest you find some time in the next 30 days to define what a perfect life means to you, then set your goals to fund it."

Mandi encouraged Michael to consider reaching out to Tonya, assuming he felt ready to invest quality time and energy into their relationship. He would need to muster up some courage for that step. He wasn't ready to risk being rejected by her again.

Steve Schlueter

Chapter 15

Running With the Pack

Friday was already off to a great start. Michael was on his weekly call with Jim Evans when Jim mentioned he was sending him a $400,000-plus seller referral. He had been making his calls, offering refinancing guidance, when a client mentioned they were planning to move out of the area, and he immediately thought of Michael. Michael remembered what Coach had said about creating a community of like-minded people. He and Jim, it occurred to him at this moment, were now part of a community. They trusted each other to care for their clients.

Michael drove along the back roads to Coach's office with a sense of peace that he hadn't felt in years. This trusted advisor approach suited him well. He was proud of himself and his "new" GMC Yukon and knew he was making great choices for his business. He was also proud of himself for taking a personal assessment of his role in the breakup with Tonya. He knew he had made some mistakes and wanted to make amends.

When Michael stepped into Coach's office, Victor was on the phone, a disappointed look on his face. Michael had never seen him in such a state. He motioned for Michael to have a seat as he wrapped up his call. He heard Victor tell the caller he was sorry things hadn't worked out and wished the person luck in their next endeavor. Victor hung up the phone, took a deep breath, and shook his head.

"What was that all about?" Michael asked.

"Well, Michael, some people just won't let go of their limiting beliefs. Remember when I said that doing the work to have a successful real estate career is simple but not easy? That's because the biggest challenge lies in managing the space between your ears. So many people allow themselves to fail because they don't want to change their habits. It's easier for them to play the victim and make excuses or justifications instead of facing reality."

Coach apologized for his rant, and said, "I had high hopes for her but today is about you. Let's dig in."

Coach asked Michael to recap the two weeks since they'd last met. Michael brought him up to speed on all of his recent successes, thanking him for teaching him about the trusted advisor approach. It had been a game-changer, and he knew this would be his way of doing business going forward. He mentioned he was also getting traction from his geo-farm and FSBO efforts.

Victor smiled and said, "I'm glad to see you're keeping up with your other leads. As much as your database is the lifeblood of your business, everyone should have one or two other strategies that are listing-specific and can be done at a reasonably high volume."

Michael looked puzzled.

"Reasonably high volume?"

Coach explained, "Not all alternate lead-generation sources are opportunity-rich right now, but the best ones will keep our database growing and can be good secondary or tertiary sources for listings. Keep up your farming, keep up your for sale by owners. Just be sure to honor the Do Not Call Laws."

The big news of the day, of course, was about the seven families coming from California. Michael told Coach about his meeting with Jeff, and how he and Jim were both working to assist the families with their transitions.

But then Coach stumped Michael with a few questions.

"Who will perform their pool maintenance? Whom will they call when they need an auto mechanic or when the heating system needs work?"

Michael looked at him blankly and said, "I have no idea. I hadn't even considered that."

"Michael, welcome to today's lesson. Building your business network, or as Mandi says, 'your **Pack**.' The members of a pack look out for one another and trust that their pack will look out for them. Your network, or 'pack,' should be made up of the business people that you trust to care for the people in your database."

Coach explained that many agents want to be part of a formal business networking group. Most often, the slot of real estate agent is the toughest position to get into because agents get in and don't leave. You're either left with the option to build your business-networking group or to not be in one.

"I want you to focus on building your business-referral network," Coach said. "This is much simpler than you might think since you already have a database that's big enough to allow you to identify your pack. As real estate agents, we're often one of the first points of contact for people moving into the area. Just think about your families from California. They'll be leaving everything behind. They'll arrive to a totally blank slate. You have the opportunity to bridge that gap between their needs and a network of great people in your local business community."

Coach continued, "Tell me, Michael, if you were a local business person that provided any kind of service, wouldn't you want to know the person who's bringing new families into our community? Think of the opportunities for those businesses to grow their customer base."

"Wow," Michael said. "I could easily add a hundred or more new business people to my network who want to know *me* because of how **I** can support *them*. That seems like a no-brainer."

Victor told Michael about hearing Gary Keller speak at a conference he attended. Gary asked the audience why Angie's List even existed when people could just ask their realtors for the help they needed. Coach explained that the key was to position ourselves as advisors and to condition our contacts to "ask you, listen to you, and trust you" to be their resource when they have housing and lifestyle needs. Building a network is a big part of being a trusted advisor.

"I know you probably didn't get into this business to be a concierge, yet this allows us to be in people's lives by serving them between transactions. This is the way to add value and earn the right to their referrals. It's a good feeling knowing that you're helping them. This week I want you to try out a new script. Now I don't want you to use this with everybody. This is just for recent clients with whom you still have a connection. I call it the '**Five-Star Conversation**.' With this conversation, your database will give you warm leads of the five-star vendors that should be in your network." Victor continued, "This way, you'll be able to provide a valuable resource to your database in the form of a client-vetted 'Five-Star Vendor Directory.' They won't need to depend on Angie's List or any other sources. They'll get conditioned to come to you."

Coach instructed Michael to go to his website, **www. neverendingreferrals.com**, click on the resources tab, and download the script. He explained how using this method could easily represent one hundred additions or more to Michael's database in just twelve to fifteen months, if he was intentional with it.

He then asked Michael how he felt about the idea of leveraging his position as a trusted advisor and combining it with building his personal business network.

"Well, I think it's a great way to broaden my database," Michael answered. "Based on what you said about a ten percent return, if I add one hundred new contacts, that's an extra ten transactions a year, a nice pay raise. Also, this feels like evidence of me being a trusted advisor instead of me just saying it. It's not about being their best friend. It's about being a local expert, which fits with who I am. I am still unclear on what to say to the business people, though."

"That's easy," Coach said. "You just go frogging."

Michael raised an eyebrow. "Frogging?"

"It's a derivation of F.O.R.D. that we use with our business relationships. F.R.O.G. It stands for **Family**, **Referral**, **Organization**, and **Goals**. Ultimately, when you have meetings with business people, you're going to go to F.R.O.G. questions to build rapport and find out about them and their business. A few examples:

Family: Did you grow up in this area?

Referral: What's the perfect referral for you?

Organization: How did the business get started?

Goals: Are you looking to expand?

"This will help you quickly create a connection with your new business relationships, particularly if they came through your database as warm contacts."

Victor suggested they set their next meeting in two weeks. He wanted Michael to have some time to work on the business networking approach before their final session.

Steve Schlueter

Chapter 16

Taming the Beast

Michael knew he was hitting his stride because he could sense how his success was annoying The Beast. Michael had just edged out Chris for top sales written that month. He had two more California buyers go under contract, and three new listings put him over the top.

One listing had come from his geo-farm. He decided he would leverage the listing with some open houses over the next two weeks to enhance his presence in the farm area. His door-knocking efforts in the farm yielded some new contacts, ones who were likely to sell their homes within a year.

Mandi helped him refine his business networking approach. Her technique for setting those appointments had worked so well that people were eager to talk to him. He set a goal to add a minimum of two new business relationships to his database each week through the end of the year. Because of his behavioral style, the business-focused conversations felt much more comfortable and genuine.

***

At the dog park, Gizmo came up to Michael and rolled over for a belly rub.

Mandi said, "Man, he never does that for anyone except me and Paul. You see, Michael, he has come to trust you. He sees the kindness you have for Sophie, and the kindness you show me here at the dog park. You've created a trusted bond with Gizmo. Just in time for your final lesson tomorrow! My nickname for that one is **40 Belly Rubs**."

Michael smiled, and said, "40 Belly Rubs! That sounds... interesting. I would ask you to explain, but I know you'll just tell me to wait to hear it from Victor!"

When the dogs ran off to play, Mandi asked about where things stood with Tonya. Had he reached out to her, and how was he feeling about that?

He said he hadn't mustered up the courage to do that yet. The idea of getting rejected again overwhelmed him.

"Well, in your own perfect time, I guess," Mandi said. "You saw what investing a little effort in your relationships has done for your business, and you know that being out of contact certainly doesn't help anything. What's the worst thing that could happen?"

Mandi gently continued down this path. "There is one thing I need to say to you, though. If you do call her, make sure you're willing to invest the energy and the time it takes to have a great relationship. It wouldn't be fair to either of you if you're not ready to put in the work. Whether it's a great business or a great relationship, you have got to make time to connect and demonstrate that you care."

Chapter 17

40 Belly Rubs

Coach and Michael greeted each other enthusiastically as they met for the last of their five lessons. Coach was proud of what Michael had accomplished over the past two months. He had transformed his business from something purely transactional to one that was centered on relationships. Even though Michael was still getting leads from FSBOs and continued working his geo-farm, it was all being done to build relationships that would last his entire career.

Victor said, "I see a lot of people who don't follow through the way you have. Those are the same people who complain that they don't get the desired results but won't admit their part in it. You, on the other hand, have done so well that I'd like to invite you to join my advanced coaching group. Normally, I would have students continue to work with a mentor, like Mandi, for another ninety days before inviting them into the group, but you've demonstrated a level of commitment that has helped you advance quickly. Are you interested in immediately continuing your journey?"

"Coach, I'm all in. Things are going well, but I know there's so much more to learn. So, yes, I'd love to sign up for the advanced coaching group. And thank you for believing in me."

"Now, I understand from Mandi that today is all about belly rubs. Coach, as much as I like you, I'm not going to lie on the floor with all fours in the air so you can give me a belly rub," Michael said jokingly.

Victor laughed and said, "And as much as I like you, Michael, I have no desire to rub your belly."

Michael replied, "That's a relief! So, what is the story with belly rubs?"

"Have you noticed how Sophie is happiest and most relaxed when you rub her belly? There are certain places on her body that she simply can't reach, so, by rolling over, she's showing that she trusts you to do for her what she doesn't know how to do for herself. And by giving her the belly rubs, you're demonstrating how much you care."

Coach continued, "I imagine you've probably heard the concept of a '36 touch,' the number of combined emails, direct mail, and personal contacts you should have with each member of your database per year?"

"Yeah, I've never put it into practice though," Michael said.

Victor shared that in their program, they subscribed to a 40-touch strategy that's both prospecting-based and marketing-enhanced. The four annual DTD2 calls make up the prospecting side of working your database, and the remaining 36 touches are the marketing-enhanced side.

"This is what I'd recommend as a marketing strategy. First, you should send out two direct mail pieces per month. Ideally, these would be hyper-local, but using a generic postcard from a mail vendor to get started is fine. Start there, and work toward more hyper-local content as soon as possible."

Eight times a year, according to Victor, Michael should send an infographic postcard with current stats for the local market.

An explanation of those stats should be printed on the backside of the postcard.

"It's not enough to just give clients raw information and stats. Being the trusted advisor means we interpret how that information impacts them. The other four months you should send out a newsletter that expands on trends, new developments, and community interest stories."

He continued, "The second direct mail piece should be a postcard that details community events, festivals, plays, and the like. On the front side, I recommend featuring a local artist, performer, or influencer, highlighting many of the great talents within the community.

"In addition to the two mailers a month, our office sends a monthly email newsletter with 3-5 topics that are relevant to our community, market trends, seasonal homeowner tips, etc. We call it our local economist newsletter. I think that's something that would work for you, too, Michael."

"When you combine the 24 direct mail pieces and the 12 emails, you've got 36 touches. Add your four DTD2s a year, and you've got your 40 belly rubs. Some agents supplement this further with college football schedules or schedules of other regional sports teams. You can take this as far as you want. Keep in mind though that the 'core 40 touch' is your foundation, and your conversations are the footings underpinning that foundation."

Michael was eager to get these next pieces in place. They made sense to him and fit with his behavioral style. He asked Coach about how to work this into his increasingly busy schedule.

"I know you mentioned that you're currently using a fee-based transaction coordinator. You could look for a virtual assistant to help with this piece. The best step you could take, however, would be to hire a personal assistant. The way your business has taken off, your biggest hurdle is going to be leverage."

Michael shared that his former assistant was working for Chris. She left him when his business slowed down, and he asked her to go part-time. She was a single mom who needed full-time employment, so she decided to work for Chris.

"She's been seeing me post all of my sales lately," Michael said. "She came to me last week and asked if I was ready to rehire her. She doesn't enjoy working for Chris. She thinks he's rude, obnoxious, and arrogant. I told her that I'd probably be ready to bring her on full-time within the next 30 days. She even offered to start working part-time for me this month until I could bring her on full-time."

They wrapped up their meeting with all the details necessary to get Michael enrolled in advanced coaching. Michael called Mary, his former assistant, when he got to the car and told her to give Chris her two weeks' notice.

As soon as he hung up with Mary, he decided there was one more call he had to make.

Chapter 18

Cafe Mimosa

Michael woke up excited to have brunch with Tonya. Their phone call had gone well, so he had taken a chance and asked her on a date. He arrived at Cafe Mimosa early to scout out the perfect table. He wanted a quiet place where they could talk. Mimosa was his favorite brunch spot because of its dog-friendly patio and excellent food. It was the perfect place for him and Tonya to catch up.

When Tonya approached the table, Michael leaned in awkwardly for a hug. He hoped he hadn't made her uncomfortable. He wanted things to go well. He eased into their conversation with safe questions, asking about Tonya's family and discussing the menu. After a few tentative minutes, they both began to relax.

Tonya smiled and said, "Tell me about Sophie! I've been checking her out on social media. I love that she has her own account. She's so cute and seems so smart. It's been fun following along as she shows off her new tricks."

Michael told Tonya that he enjoyed training Sophie because she was such a quick study. He had also realized that the process of training her had caused him to adopt better discipline for his own life. Going on daily walks also meant that they were both getting more exercise and fresh air now. Overall, Sophie had been a great addition to his life.

Tonya asked what made Michael decide to get a dog, and he admitted that he had been lonely after she left. He explained that working with Sophie had helped keep his spirits up during that rough time.

"It makes me smile when I walk through the door and Sophie is excited to see me. She always greets me with a little happy dance. It's much better than walking into an empty house."

The server arrived with their meals and refilled their coffees. It was Tonya's first time at Mimosa, and Michael was relieved that she was enjoying herself.

Between bites, Tonya grinned and said, "You'll never guess what I got!"

She pulled out her phone, flashed a picture of an adorable little Dachshund, and said, "This is Sammie, Isn't he the cutest? I saw his picture online, and knew I had to have him."

"Wow! He is cute. I never realized you wanted a dog."

"Well, in a way, you and Sophie led me to him. I had been thinking about getting a dog but hadn't even thought about checking the animal shelters. After doing some research, I realized how many sweet animals there are who just need a second chance."

As they continued to chat, Tonya noticed Michael's attentiveness. He used to worry so much about business and the next deal, and he could never seem to focus on being present. She liked his new attitude and wondered what had changed. She wondered if Michael deserved a *second chance*, too.

She asked, "What else have you been up to, besides hanging out with Sophie?"

Michael told her about Mandi, Victor, and Jim, and the impact they were having on his life and business. He talked about the freedom he felt now that he could attract business instead of chasing it.

He asked how things were going with her physical therapy practice. It just so happened that she had so many referrals and repeat clients that she had hired two physical therapists and an office manager. She had transformed her small practice into a thriving business. Michael always knew that Tonya would be a success since she was wired for relationship-building and took excellent care of her patients.

After two more cups of coffee and a lot more conversation, Michael noticed that he and Tonya were the last diners on the patio. The brunch crowd had scattered, and it was time to say goodbye.

He looked at Tonya and said, "It was great seeing you today. Before you go, there's something I need to say. I'm sorry that I took you for granted. I've thought a lot about how I acted when we were together, and I apologize. I want to thank you for being part of my life, and for putting up with me for those two years. I miss you and would love to see you again, assuming you're willing to give me a *second chance*."

Tonya liked the Michael that showed up that day, but she hadn't forgotten about their time together. She wasn't willing to go back to being low woman on his priority list, so she needed to feel sure that things had truly changed.

"I had a nice time today, and I'd like to see you again, but I think we should take it slow. Maybe we can take Sammie and Sophie to the dog park tomorrow?"

They agreed to meet at the dog park the next morning since Michael had an appointment with one of his California buyers in the afternoon.

Steve Schlueter

Chapter 19

Check Your Ego

As September came to a close, Victor asked his students to carefully review quarter three and begin to look ahead to the coming year. He explained that to meet goals the following year it was important to finish the current year strong.

"Ideally," Victor said, "you should establish your annual goal, then aim to have ten to fifteen percent of that goal in pending transactions on January 1."

Michael was proud of his third-quarter results. It had been the best third quarter he'd ever had, and he was on track to have his second-best year ever. The Beast was just ahead of him in production. As Michael looked at his pending business, he felt pretty certain that he could overtake Chris if he focused during the fourth quarter. He committed to doubling down on his lead generation with FSBOs. He thought that if he found a few of those, and stepped up his geo-farming, he could likely knock Chris out of first place.

Michael caught himself going into ego mode, and suddenly remembered the tale of Icarus, the overconfident young man who flew too close to the sun.

He thought to himself, "This shouldn't be about me over-reaching. It's about me being true to myself, and to the business I'm building. It's about having a healthy and balanced life."

With that, he decided not to go on an ego chase. He resolved to keep working on the plan Victor had shown him.

Transforming himself and his business had been hard work. He felt grateful to have his assistant, Mary, back with him. Everything that she'd put in place allowed his "40-Touch System" to function at a high level. They were using a virtual transaction coordinator, so Mary could focus on the systems that Michael was learning in his advanced coaching sessions.

Victor challenged Michael to add a client event to his fourth-quarter approach. Michael and Mary decided to host a pie party near the end of November. They outlined all the *touches* related to the event because Victor had taught him that *the event* is about more than just the actual event.

"Events are a great way to show appreciation and support, and they're also an opportunity to strengthen existing relationships and develop new ones. Even those clients that can't make it to the event appreciate being invited," Victor had said.

Mandi gave Michael and Mary some great tips on event planning since she was somewhat of an expert on the subject. She suggested that he double down on his DTD2, doing what she called "DTD4." She said he should contact everyone in his database before the event so that he would be done with all his fourth-quarter calls by Thanksgiving. This would do two things, she explained. It would allow him to invite all his clients to the event as part of his regular call schedule, and free him up to take some time off during the holidays. He knew Tonya would be happy about that second point.

Michael and Tonya spent the last half of the year rebuilding their relationship. They even attended Victor's couples' retreat in October. Michael worked hard to be the present and attentive partner that Tonya deserved. He started taking Sundays off so that he and Tonya could spend time with her family. He was surprised to discover that taking time *away* from the businesses didn't just make him a better boyfriend but made him a better *businessperson* as well.

Steve Schlueter

Chapter 20

New Year, New You

It was Sunday, January 1, the first day of the next year. Michael Barnes sat at his desk, wearing his favorite grey sweats and warm sheepskin slippers. It was a clear and bright morning with no chance of rain. He watched as the marshmallows dissolved into froth on the surface of his hot chocolate. As he glanced at his calendar, he realized that he'd never been more ready to turn the page than he was that day. The past year had been transformational, and he knew that the next year would be his best yet.

Michael's business was thriving. He'd managed to earn a good living, and he felt proud. He thought back over the year and was grateful to those who helped him along the way. He certainly had his share of obstacles to overcome.

Michael smiled as he remembered the day, almost exactly a year before, when Mandi and Gizmo came through the gate and into the small dog area.

Steve Schlueter

Quick Reference Guide

The System Fundamentals

F.O.R.D. (Chapter 8):
The Art and Science of Sales Dialogue

The F.O.R.D. Method is a critical tool for turning scripts into conversations. You can enhance the quality of your conversations by building questions around the following topics:

Family (or Friends)
Occupation
Recreation
Dreams

DTD2/Three Attempt Approach
(Chapters 7 & 10)

Using the **DTD2** system and a three-attempt approach each week allows you to build a perpetual pipeline of business.
You can find the DTD2 schedule, theme-based graphics, sample scripts, and more on the "free resources" page of our website.

Behavior and the Trusted Advisor
(Chapters 11 & 12)

Every behavioral style has the potential for limiting beliefs. Fortunately, there are tools available to help us adapt our behaviors while remaining authentic.

Taking a behavior assessment and participating in our group-coaching program can help you understand your own behavior and the behaviors of those in our database.

This is covered in depth in Session 2 of our coaching program.

Business Network/F.R.O.G. (Chapter 15)

As real estate professionals, we are one of the first points of contact for someone moving into the area. Building a list of trusted business contacts serves two purposes. First, it allows you to assist your clients with recommendations. Second, it builds reciprocity among the business community.

Download the "5-Star Script" to assist you in identifying those business relationships on our "free-resources" page of our website.

40-Touch System (Chapter 17)

Regular contact with your database is the key to repeat business and referrals. Our **40-touch workshop** (Session 6 of our group coaching program) will help you craft your personal marketing message and teach you the best delivery methods and schedule.

The Never-Ending Referrals Community

The greatest gift for us is watching our students succeed and thrive with their relationships while creating a business of *Never-Ending Referrals*. Tammi Juengst and I have made real estate sales a lifetime study, and we would like to invite you to continue your journey with us so we can show you the systems, tools, and conversations that will give you the confidence to engage your database at the highest level. To find out more about how you can enroll in our coaching community visit us at

www.NeverEndingReferrals.com

Community member benefits include:

24/7 E-Learning Portal with over 100 Video Lessons
Live Session 3 X Per Month on the 8 Lessons of NER
3 x Per Month Live Interviews / Topic Deep Dives
Quarterly Market of the Moment Scripts (Conversations)
Never Ending Referrals VIP Facebook Group
Tech Tutorials that keep things simple
Marketing Sample Scrapbook
Low Monthly Membership Fee

Free-Resources
Visit **www.NeverEndingReferrals.com/resources**
for free tools and resources.

Events and Keynotes

You can hire Steve or Tammi for a *Never Ending Referrals* live event for your local association, region or conference. Send your inquiry to **info@NeverEndingReferrals.com**

Steve Schlueter

Acknowledgements

Tammi Juengst, my co-coach of our *Never Ending Referrals* coaching program. You are an amazing mastermind partner, gifted coach, and trusted friend. Your influences are all over "Rescue Dogs and Real Estate".

Avis Wukasch, you are the definition of passionate, and your ability to champion the causes of both realtors and consumers on a daily basis amazes me. Your influence and drive has led us to becoming the dominant real estate brokerage in Williamson County, TX.

Thank you Richard and Judy Copple for taking a chance on a young guy opening a real estate office in Round Rock, TX. You immediately validated us and contributed to our quick growth. Thank you for trusting our vision and being a part of it.

A special thanks to our brokerage leadership team who work tirelessly every day to serve our 400+ associates: Kasey Jorgenson, Mary Thornton, Kriston Wood, Kari Christ, Candie Shelton, April Freese, Bruce Rodden, Ryann Hudson, Donna Arltd, Lauren Sansing, Jennifer Locklin, Monica Pride, Michele Sherwood, Rachael Payton, Mary Zumwalt, Jeff Sralla, Julie Jones, and Marie Dahmer.

Thank you to Steve and Judy Scott, my first brokers, for your encouragement. Thank you, Barbara Hill and Bob and Maria

Holzmueller for your pioneering spirits and serving as my brokers prior to Keller Williams.

Thank you, Mike Ferry, Howard Brinton, Rick DeLuca, Tony Robbins, Floyd Wickman, Dianna Kokoska, Michael Gerber, Walter Sandford, and Monica Reynolds for the early training that set the foundation for my sales career.

Thank you, Gary Keller, Mark Willis, Mo Anderson, Wendi Harrelson, Mona Covey, and so many more at KWRI who have contributed to my leadership growth and opportunities.

I want to thank my coaches and mentors Pat Mancuso, Debbie Frapp, Ron Patulski, John Prescott, Dianna Kokoska, Monica Reynolds, Debbie De Grote, Mary Tennant, and Tony DiCello. No one succeeds alone and our coaches are truly the wind beneath our wings.

Thank you to Monica Reynolds, Sajag Patel, and Fritz Pollard, and the amazing MAPS Coaches and staff for championing our *Never Ending Referrals* coaching program.

A special shout out to my fellow road-warrior BOLD Coaches, led by Scott Toombs. What you do to transform lives is utterly profound.

To all those that share the same passion for building a relationship-based business and have influenced my thinking in this space, thank you. Larry Kendall, author of *Ninja Selling*; Michael J. Maher, author of *7 Levels of Communication*; Brian Buffini, Joe Stumpf, Gary Keller, Dave Jenks, and Jay Papasan, co-authors of *The Millionaire Real Estate Agent*; Mary Harker, Alyce and Seth Dailey, Judy Johns and family, and, of course, Gerri Misko, my original mentor who helped me find my way.

Thank you Avner Landes for editing and tightening the manuscript.

Our rescue dogs, Sophie and Chico, and Tammi's beloved

rescue dog, Gizmo, helped inspire our story. They truly are our loyal companions.

I'm grateful for the wisdom of Shelly's late father, Clyde Dent, who was the perfect example of a giver, and to our adult children, Meaghan, Maggie, Jennifer, Stephanie, Chad, and Eric, who remind us what matters.

And finally: Shelly Shea. Thank you for your exceptional editing skills, the many evenings and weekends spent helping me bring Michael's story to life, and for saving my readers from too much *mansplaining*! Most importantly, thank you for being my partner in life. I'm blessed to have found my soulmate.

Steve Schlueter

About the Author

STEVE SCHLUETER is the founder and co-coach of Never Ending Referrals. He is a real estate coach, trainer, and multi-office brokerage operator with more than 14,000 hours experience coaching and training real estate agents and industry leaders.

As an agent, he sold as many as 100 homes a year before transitioning into a leadership role at the Keller Williams Northwest office in Austin, Texas. He led the early development of a KW region and became a KW MAPS coach and a member of the Keller Williams University Master Faculty.

Steve lives in San Antonio, TX with his partner, Shelly Shea, and their four-legged family members, Sophie and Chico.

To learn more about
Steve and Never Ending Referrals, please visit

www.NeverEndingReferrals.com

Made in the USA
Middletown, DE
09 September 2021